3-DIMENSIONAL TEACHING & LEARNING®

GRADE 5
Life Science
Activity Book

Knowing Science®
3-DIMENSIONAL TEACHING & LEARNING

KS

GRADE 5
Life Science Activity Book

Developed by

William Banko, M.D.

Dario Capasso, Ph.D.

Editors

Sarah McGinnis

Lesley Quattrone

Written by

Jennifer Baxter

Sarah McGinnis

Helen Pashley, Ph.D.

Jeffrey S. Schwartz

Advisors

Michael E. Jabot, Ph.D.
Professor, Science Education
Director, Institute for Research in Science Teaching
State University of New York at Fredonia

Thomas O'Brien, Ph.D.
Professor, Science Education
Department of Teaching, Learning & Educational Leadership
Binghamton University, Binghamton, New York

Knowing Science, LLC - Armonk, NY USA
www.knowingscience.com

Cover and Teacher's Manual Design:

Page Designs Inc.

www.pagedesignsinc.com

Table of Contents

GRADE 5

Life Science Activity Book

UNIT 1: MATTER AND ENERGY IN ORGANISMS AND ECOSYSTEMS

1.1 Food Webs and Energy

VOCABULARY

Using correct vocabulary can help you understand science concepts better. Below are some important terms that you will learn about in *Lesson 1.1 Food Webs and Energy.* Study the words and their definitions, and try to use them whenever you talk about these topics during the lesson!

Abiotic: *(adj.)* Relating to nonliving organisms.

Biome: *(noun)* A large community of plants and animals that occupy a distinct region such as a desert, a rainforest, or a freshwater lake.

Biotic: *(adj.)* Relating to living organisms.

Carbon dioxide: *(noun)* A naturally occurring chemical compound composed of 2 oxygen atoms connected to a single carbon atom. It is normally found in its gas form.

Carnivore: *(noun)* An animal that eats only meat.

Chlorophyll: *(noun)* The green substance in plants that uses light to manufacture food from carbon dioxide and water.

Consumer: *(noun)* An organism that feeds on other organisms or particles of organic matter.

Decomposer: *(noun)* An organism, often a bacterium or fungus, that feeds on and breaks down dead plant or animal matter. Decomposers make essential nutrients available to plants and other organisms in the ecosystem.

Ecosystem: *(noun)* All the living things in a place and their relation to their environment.

Energy (biology): *(noun)* In form of nutrients and sunlight is what sustains plants and animals in living.

Food chain: *(noun)* An ordered arrangement of animals and plants in which each feeds on the one below it in the chain.

Food web: *(noun)* The complex network of related food chains within an ecosystem.

Habitat: *(noun)* Place where animals or plants live and interact.

Herbivore: *(noun)* An animal that only eats plants.

Invasive: *(adj.)* Plants or animals that take over in areas where they do not normally live. Invasive plants or animals may have a big effect on the ecosystem.

Limiting factor: *(noun)* An environmental factor that affects the survival of living things and restricts the size of a population; for example: a limited amount of resources.

Niche: *(noun)* The specific role that a plant or animal has within an ecosystem; i.e., where an organism lives and how it obtains food.

Nutrients: *(noun)* Substances such as proteins, minerals, or vitamins that are needed by people, animals, and plants to stay strong and healthy.

Omnivore: *(noun)* An animal that eats both plants and meat.

Oxygen: *(noun)* A naturally occurring chemical compound composed of 2 oxygen atoms. It is normally found in its gas form.

Photosynthesis: *(noun)* A chemical process by which green plants and some other organisms make their food. Plants use energy from the Sun to turn water and carbon dioxide into food, and they produce oxygen as a by-product.

Producer: *(noun)* An organism that produces its own food and serves as a source of food for other organisms. Producers include green plants, which produce food through photosynthesis, and certain bacteria that are capable of converting inorganic substances into food through chemosynthesis.

Pyramid (Biology): *(noun)* A graphical representation designed to show the number of animals in a food web. Also known as an energy or food pyramid. Producers make up the bottom of the pyramid, since they are found in large numbers. The number of consumers is fewer and decreases the further up the pyramid you go.

Scavenger: *(noun)* An animal that feeds on organisms that have already died or that have been killed by another animal. Vultures and hyenas are scavengers.

Species: *(noun)* A group of living things that share certain traits and can produce offspring.

Name_____

Directions: Cut out the cards below. Can you think of different ways that these organisms could be grouped? Try sorting the cards a few times in different ways, and be ready to explain what you did.

Seaweed	Octopus	Moray Eel	Coral
Parrotfish	Polar Bear	Seal	Arctic Fox
Codfish	Arctic Hare	Grasshopper	Earthworm
Jackrabbit	Water lily	Minnow	Lizard
Owl	Cactus	Scorpion	Beetle

Activity Sheet 2: Interdependency

Name _____

Directions: Read the text, paying attention to vocabulary in **bold** print. Then answer the questions on the following page.

What is Interdependency?

What exactly is interdependency? Many of the plants and animals that you sorted in the previous activity are **interdependent**. This means that they rely on one another to meet their basic needs for survival.

Living things depend not only on each other for survival, but also on the nonliving parts of their ecosystem: water, air, and nutrients found in soil. An **ecosystem** includes the living and nonliving parts of a particular area that are interdependent. The boundaries of any ecosystem are not clearly defined, and organisms may move between ecosystems. Thus, any ecosystem is constantly changing, if only slightly.

There are several sub-groups within any ecosystem. A **habitat** is a specific area where a specific plant or animal lives most of the time. A tree can be a habitat for a squirrel, and soil can be a habitat for a beetle. A **species** is a group of the same type of organism that can produce offspring, such as bluebirds, mice, or dandelions. The number of a particular species that lives in an ecosystem is called a **population**. All the populations of all the living things (plants and animals) in a specific area make up a **community**.

Every plant and every animal has its own specific role within an ecosystem, relating to where it lives and how it obtains food. This role is called a **niche**. Many times (but not always), an organism's niche is important to the survival of other organisms.

Ecosystems can be grouped into land and water categories. **Terrestrial ecosystems** include deciduous forests, rainforests, deserts, and grasslands. **Freshwater ecosystems** include ponds or lakes, rivers, and marshes. Saltwater ecosystems are found in the Earth's oceans.

Scientists have divided our world into different biomes, as well. A **biome** is a group of several similar ecosystems. While an ecosystem may cover only a small area, such as a local forest, a biome covers a much larger geographic area, such the Amazon Rainforest or the Sahara Desert. No matter where plants or animals live, whether in a deciduous forest or in a coral reef, they still rely on other organisms to survive. They are all interdependent.

Directions: Define each vocabulary word by filling out the graphic organizer.

Species		**Population**
	Ecosystem	
Community		**Niche**

Directions: There are several different types of ecosystems. List each example that was mentioned in the text under its correct heading.

Land Ecosystems	Water Ecosystems

Activity Sheet 3: The Photosynthesis Equation

Name_____

Directions: Read the text, paying attention to the vocabulary in **bold** print.

The Photosynthesis Equation

All living things need energy to live and grow, but plants and animals get their energy in different ways. Animals are able to move from place to place to find food. But plants cannot move from place to place. Instead, they need to manufacture their own food.

Photosynthesis is the process that plants use to manufacture food. Photo means "light" and synthesis means "to put together." Plants need three ingredients for photosynthesis: sunlight, carbon dioxide, and water.

The first ingredient is **sunlight**. Plants absorb energy from the Sun. Inside a leaf are special cells called chloroplasts. These chloroplasts contain a green substance called **chlorophyll**. It is the chlorophyll that helps a plant absorb solar energy. It also gives leaves their green color. Green leaves show that a plant is producing food.

Carbon dioxide is the second ingredient needed for photosynthesis. Plants "breathe" through openings on the undersides of their leaves. Air moves into the leaves. Carbon dioxide is removed from the air and **oxygen** is "exhaled" by the plant.

The third ingredient is **water**. The plant's roots absorb water from the soil. The water travels up the stem through special tubes called **xylem** ("zy-lem"). Water combines with carbon dioxide and solar energy collected in the leaves to produce a kind of sugar called **glucose**. Glucose is the plant's food. The glucose is transported from the leaves to all parts of the plant through special tubes called **phloem** ("flow-em"). Extra food is stored in roots and stems. All together, the photosynthesis "equation" looks like this:

solar energy + carbon dioxide + water + chlorophyll = glucose sugar + oxygen

The process of plant photosynthesis is very important not only for plants, but also for animals, including humans. Much of the oxygen that animals and humans breathe is the result of photosynthesis. Plants are also a major food source for many animals. Humans and many animals eat plants to get food energy. Plants get their energy for photosynthesis from the Sun, which helps the plants make food and grow. So if you think about it, most of the energy used by living things comes from the Sun, either directly or indirectly. Photosynthesis is a mysterious process, which scientists are still trying to figure out.

 Here's something to think about the next time you're hungry... As a human, you probably go to the kitchen to grab a snack. But if you were a plant, you would absorb some water through your roots, breathe through your leaves, and turn towards the Sun to make your own food!

Photosynthesis Equation Questions

Directions: Use the text to fill in the diagram below, and then answer the questions that follow.

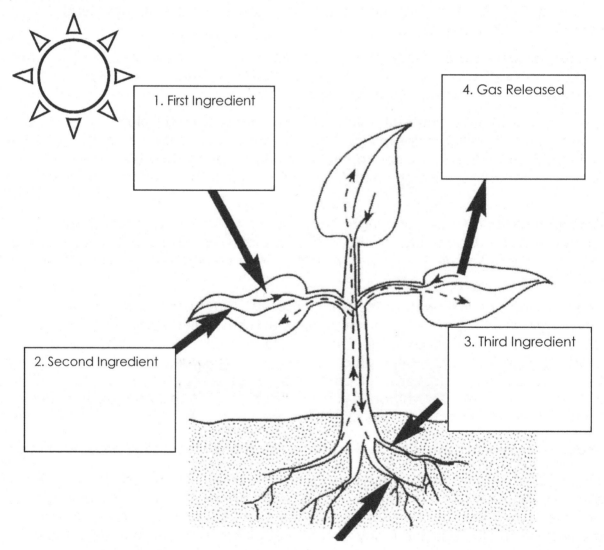

1. First Ingredient

4. Gas Released

2. Second Ingredient

3. Third Ingredient

1. Why do plants need to manufacture their own food?

   _____

   _____

   _____

2. What three ingredients are needed for photosynthesis?

   _____

   _____

3. What is the name of the food manufactured by the plant during photosynthesis?

   _____

   _____

4. Why is photosynthesis important for animals and humans?

   _____

   _____

   _____

   _____

Activity Sheet 4: "Seeing Green"

Name_____

Directions: Complete the following activities and record your observations. Then answer the questions.

Question: What is needed for photosynthesis to take place?

Materials:

2 green leaves	2 plastic containers	1 cardboard box	water
1 green plant	1 aluminum foil sheet	paperclips	

Procedure:

1. Fill the plastic containers about ¾ of the way with water. Place one green leaf in each container.

2. Place one of the containers under the cardboard box, and place the other in a sunny location. You may choose to make a "before" drawing in your science notebook.

3. Now take the aluminum foil, and cut or tear it into little squares. Place an aluminum square on top of one or two of the green plant's leaves. Secure the squares using the paperclips to make sure that no light gets in.

4. Set the plant in a sunny location. Be sure to keep the plant watered. You may choose to make a "before" drawing in your science notebook.

5. Make predictions about what will happen to each of the leaves.

6. After about an hour, observe the "sunny" leaf and the "dark" leaf. After a week, observe the aluminum-covered leaves. What do you notice about each of the leaves? You may choose to make an "after" drawing of each in your science notebook.

7. Record your observations and conclusions below.

Predictions: What will happen to each of the leaves?

"Sunny" leaf:

_____

"Dark" leaf:

_____

Leaves covered with aluminum foil:

_____

Observations:

How did the leaves change? Which ingredient for photosynthesis was missing for the "dark" leaf and the aluminum-covered leaves?

_____

_____

_____

_____

_____

Conclusions:

What is necessary for photosynthesis to take place? What happens if an ingredient is removed?

_____

_____

_____

_____

Name _____

Directions: Read the text, paying close attention to the diagrams and any vocabulary in **bold** print.

Food Webs and Interdependence

All organisms – plants and animals – need food energy (nutrients) to survive. But the way these organisms obtain food energy differs. Plants make their own food through the process of photosynthesis. Using water, carbon dioxide, and sunlight, plants make glucose, which is stored in the plant's stems and roots. Because plants produce their own food, they are called **producers**.

Animals, however, cannot make their own food. They must get their nutrients (food energy) by eating plants or other animals. Organisms that eat other organisms for energy are called **consumers**. Some consumers eat only plants. They are called **primary consumers**, or **herbivores**. Deer, cows, and rabbits are all herbivores. Any animal that eats another animal is called a **secondary consumer**, or **carnivore**. Hawks, lions, and wolves are carnivores. Some organisms eat both plants and animals. They are called **omnivores**. Humans, bears, and birds are omnivores.

Other organisms get their food energy from dead organisms or plant and animal waste. These organisms are called **decomposers**. Worms, mushrooms, and bacteria are all decomposers. Decomposers are important because they return nutrients to the soil, so that they can be used by plants.

A **food chain** shows how energy is passed from the Sun to producers, consumers, and decomposers. All food chains begin with the Sun. Here is an example of a food chain:

Sun ➔ grass ➔ cricket ➔ frog ➔ snake ➔ earthworm

After the snake dies, the earthworm will feed on it and return nutrients to the soil, which will be used by the grass. The energy path continues.

In nature, many organisms eat more than one kind of food. Food chains overlap and combine. When this happens, the food chains form a **food web**. A food web shows many different feeding relationships. It includes all the producers, consumers, and decomposers that live in a particular area, or ecosystem. On the next page is an example of a food web.

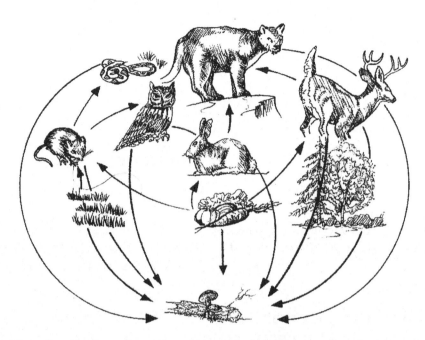

The plants and animals in a food web are **interdependent**, meaning they need each other for survival. Primary consumers obtain food energy from plants. Energy is then passed to secondary consumers, which get their food energy by eating the primary consumers. Decomposers get their energy from both producers and consumers, and then return energy/ nutrients to the soil for producers to use again.

If one organism is removed from the food web, the flow of energy will be changed. All the other organisms will be affected.

Questions: Use the text and diagrams to answer the following questions.

1. What does a food web show?

_____

_____

_____

Directions: The table below lists all the organisms pictured in the food web above. Use the table and the food web diagram to answer the questions:

Plants	Animals	Decomposers
Grass Green leaves Vegetables	Mouse Owl Rabbit Deer Snake Mountain lion	Mushrooms

1. Which of these organisms are producers? How do they obtain their food energy?

_____

_____

2. According to the graphic, which organisms are carnivores, which are herbivores, and which are omnivores?

Carnivores: _____

Herbivores: _____

Omnivores: _____

3. Which of these organisms obtain their food energy from waste or dead organisms?

_____

_____

4. How do decomposers help producers?

_____

_____

5. How does food energy get from one organism to another?

_____

_____

_____

_____

_____

Activity Sheet 6: Food Web Cards

sun	water lily	green plant
	producer	producer

snail	duckweed	tadpole	duck
water plants	producer	water plants small snails	water plants, small fish, insects, tadpoles

perch	turtle	crayfish	frog
tadpoles, snails, crayfish	snails, tadpoles, water plants	tadpoles, beetles, snails	mosquitoes worms

mosquito	salamander	worm	beetle
plant nectar, animal blood	insects, tadpoles, snails, worms	decomposer	decomposer

Activity Sheet 7: Clean Up Crew

Name _____

Directions: Read the text about scavengers and decomposers, paying close attention to vocabulary in **bold** print. Then, fill in the graphic organizer.

Scavengers and Decomposers: Sanitation Engineers

What happens if an organism dies without being eaten, or is not completely eaten by an animal? Nature's sanitation engineers are on the job! Scavengers and decomposers are organisms that obtain their food energy from the remains of plants and animals.

Scavengers are animals that eat other animals that are already dead. Vultures, coyotes, crayfish, and crows are all scavengers. As they eat, they help break the organisms down into smaller pieces. Then it is the decomposers' turn.

Decomposers eat the smaller pieces and break them down even further into nutrients. They return these nutrients to the soil through their waste material. Earthworms and insects, such as ants, flies, and beetles, are first-level decomposers. Earthworms are especially important: in addition to returning nutrients to the soil, they also help loosen the soil so that water and air can circulate through it.

Fungi, such as mushrooms, and many bacteria, such as yeast, are the next level of decomposers. They break the organic material down to a chemical level. Some food energy is absorbed for their own survival, but much is released back into the soil.

Plants use chemical nutrients from the soil for the process of photosynthesis, and so the nutrients are recycled back into food chains and food webs. Without scavengers and decomposers, land and water ecosystems would be filled with dead plants and animals. Plants would find it difficult to obtain the nutrients they need for survival, which would negatively affect all food chains/webs. Who knew bacteria, fungi, and worms were so important?

Fill in the graphic organizer:

	Roles	Examples
Scavengers		
First-level decomposers		
Second-level decomposers		

Activity Sheet 8: Rotten Bananas

Name _____

Directions: Follow directions for this investigation to learn more about decomposition.

Question: How can we speed up the process of decomposition?

Materials:

- ✓ 2 zipper bags
- ✓ 4 banana slices
- ✓ dry yeast
- ✓ measuring spoon
- ✓ permanent marker

Procedure:

1. Label one zipper bag "Yeast" and the other bag "No yeast."

2. Place two banana slices in each zipper bag.

3. Sprinkle ½ teaspoon of yeast on the banana slices in the "Yeast" bag.

4. Seal the zipper bags and put them in a place where they can be observed each day.

5. Observe each day for about one week. Record your observations in the chart on the next page.

Day	Observations	Quick Sketch	
		Yeast	No Yeast
1			
2			
3			
4			
5			
6			
7			

Observations:

1. Which banana slices showed evidence of change first?

   _____

   _____

2. Which banana slices showed more evidence of change?

   _____

   _____

3. What evidence of decomposition did you see? How did the yeast change the banana slices?

   _____

   _____

   _____

   _____

   _____

4. Yeast is a kind of fungus, in the same group as mushrooms. Where does the yeast get its food energy?

   _____

   _____

5. If this banana was outside decomposing, how might it help other plants?

   _____

   _____

Conclusions: What role do decomposers play in the process of breaking down organic material?

_____

_____

_____

_____

_____

Activity Sheet 9: Energy and Limiting Factors

Name _____

Directions: Read the text, paying attention to the vocabulary in bold print. Then answer the questions that follow.

Energy and Limiting Factors

All living things depend on energy obtained from food for survival. Food energy is used during all life processes; growth, eating, moving, breathing, and even sleeping. An **energy pyramid** shows the direction in which energy is passed through any food web. The size of each level of the pyramid represents the relative number of organisms at that level, as well as the amount of energy available to the organisms at that level.

Every food web starts with energy from the Sun. This energy is used by producers to manufacture their own food. Some food energy is used to live and grow. A plant stores only about 10% of the food it produces in its leaves, roots, and stem. It uses the other 90% for growth.

Producers form the base of any energy pyramid. This level has the most energy because it has the most organisms. When a primary consumer, or herbivore, eats plant material, the energy stored in the plant is passed along. The primary consumer uses most of this energy for its life processes. The rest (again, only about 10%) is stored in the animal's body.

When a secondary consumer, or carnivore, eats a primary consumer, the 10% stored energy is passed along. The secondary consumer uses 90% of the energy it obtains from eating other animals. It stores the other 10%.

Thus, the total amount of energy decreases as it is passed through each level. Most energy pyramids support only four to five levels.

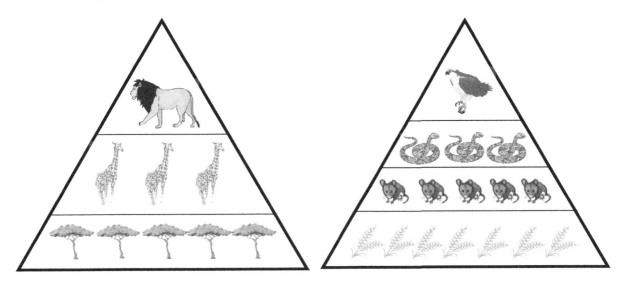

If any one part of a food web is disrupted, the movement of energy is also disrupted. Those affects may be felt through the rest of the food web. This can happen in many ways.

Limiting factors include the availability of food, water, sunlight, temperature, shelter, or space in an ecosystem. They affect the balance of any food web in an ecosystem. **Biotic factors** include any plants or animals. **Abiotic factors** are the nonliving parts of an ecosystem, and may include the amount and quality of water, soil, or even air.

All ecosystems change over time. **Natural changes** in temperature, rainfall, or soil conditions may affect plant and animal populations. **Natural disasters** change ecosystems quickly. If conditions change enough, organisms may not be able to meet their needs. If possible, they can move to another area with more resources; otherwise, they will probably die. Changes in plant or animal populations will affect food chains and food webs.

Humans may also affect ecosystems. Habitat destruction, pollution, and hunting all affect the balance of populations in any ecosystem. Sometimes **invasive species** are introduced from another ecosystem. Because they are not part of any natural food webs in the new ecosystem, these species may change the eating patterns of native primary or secondary consumers.

1. How is an energy pyramid different from a food web?

   _____

   _____

   _____

   _____

   _____

2. Why is each level of an energy pyramid narrower than the level below it?

   _____

   _____

   _____

   _____

   _____

   _____

   _____

3. Fill in the graphic organizer below using information from the text:

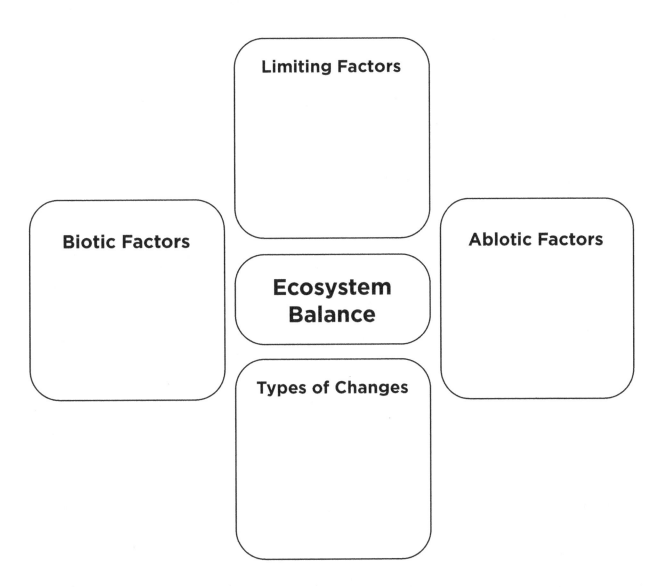

Activity Sheet 10: Limiting Factors Game

Name _____

Direction: Read the rules for "How Many for Dinner?" After playing the game, answer the questions.

How Many for Dinner?

In any ecosystem, limiting factors (such as food, water, weather conditions or human activity) affect populations of plants and animals, predators and prey. During this game, you will be a member of a herd of herbivores in any ecosystem.

Materials:

- ✓ Poker chips; there must be 30 of one color and 10 more of any other combination of colors.
- ✓ Bag

The Game:

1. Put the 30 same-colored chips or cubes into the bag. Then put 5 of the other-colored chips into the bag. The chips should not be visible as herd "members" draw them out of the bag.

2. The 30 same-colored chips represent food for the animals. The other-colored chips represent limiting factors, such as extreme weather conditions, invasive species, predators, human hunters, habitat destruction, or pollution.

3. Start with a "herd" of 15 players.

4. Round 1:
   - Each member of the herd must draw two chips. These two chips represent enough food for survival through a season.
   - If both chips are the same-color "food chips," the animal survives. If one or both is a "limiting factor chip," the animal "dies" and is out of the game (at least for this round).
   - After each member has had a turn, return all chips to the bag.

5. Round 2:
   - Add some new herd members; half as many as survived the winter. These additional members represent offspring born the following spring. (For example, if 13 survived the winter, add 6 more offspring. If 15 survived the winter, add 7 offspring.)

- Each herd member should draw two chips. As before, two food chips means survival, while one or more predator chips means that the herd member dies and is out of the round.
- If the chips run out before the end of the round, this means that any member that didn't get to draw chips dies because it couldn't find food.

6. Round 3:
   - Add 10 more members from a nearby herd. They have been forced out of their habitat due to predators or a possible food shortage.
   - Each herd member should draw two chips. Again, two food chips means survival, while one or more predator chips means death.
   - If the chips run out before the end of the round, this means that any member that didn't get to draw chips dies because it couldn't find food.

7. Round 4:
   - Add the other 5 predator chips. These chips represent the arrival of 5 new predators (or hunters) that have come to hunt the larger herd.
   - Each herd member should draw two chips. Once again, two food chips means survival, while one or more predator chips means death.

8. The game may conclude here, or you may continue playing with other variations in limiting factors decided by the group.

Questions:

1. What caused fluctuations in the population of the herd?

   _____

   _____

2. What limiting factors came into play?

   _____

   _____

3. How did the predator/prey variation affect the herd?

   _____

   _____

   _____

4. How could this happen in an actual habitat?

_____

_____

_____

_____

5. What other variables might affect the population of the herd?

_____

_____

_____

_____

Activity Sheet 11: Ecosystem Trading Cards

Name _____

Directions: Read about how to create ecosystem trading cards.

Ecosystem Trading Cards

1. Work in groups of 4-6. Choose an ecosystem or draw one randomly.

2. Preview the lists of plants and animals provided on the next page to help you get started. You may add more organisms from your own research.

3. Use the trading card template to list facts about the organisms in your ecosystem. Your group can decide what size to make the actual trading cards.

4. Include clipart, drawings, or images from the Internet.

5. After your trading cards are complete, use information from them to create an ecosystem food web poster. Start with the Sun at the top, and put the producers just below it. Primary consumers come next, followed by secondary consumers. Scavengers/ decomposers go at the bottom.

6. Include a background setting to show the abiotic parts of the ecosystem.

7. Be ready to present your trading cards and food web to the class!

Arctic Tundra		Desert	
polar bear	arctic hare	coyote	kit fox
arctic fox	snowy owl	jackrabbit	scorpion
arctic squirrel	moss lichen	elf owl	sagebrush
		desert cricket	cactus

Temperate Forest		Rainforest	
oak tree	maple tree	orangutan	sloth
fern	squirrel	howler monkey	toucan
deer	coyote	jaguar	butterfly
grasshopper	hawk	tree frog	epiphytes
skunk	mouse		

Freshwater Pond		Coral Reef	
duckweed	water lily	coral	anemone
snail	tadpole	octopus	parrot fish
perch	duck	starfish	seahorse
salamander	beetle	reef lobster	algae

Prairie Grassland		African Grassland	
prairie dog	snake	lion	giraffe
grasses	clover	hyena	antelope
hawk	mouse	elephant	jackal
grasshopper	fungi	grasses	acacia tree

Trading Card Template

Plant/Animal Name

Illustration - What Does It Look Like?

Habitat:

Physical Characteristics:

Diet: (producer; carni-/herbi-/omnivore)

Prey: (if any)

Predators: (if any)

Interesting Facts:

1.2 Owl Pellets

VOCABULARY

Using correct vocabulary can help you understand science concepts better. Below are some important terms that you will learn about in *Lesson 1.2 Owl Pellets*. Study the words and their definitions, and try to use them whenever you talk about these topics during the lesson!

Adaptation: *(noun)* A change by which an organism or species becomes better suited to its environment.

Camouflage: *(noun)* The physical appearance or features that allow certain animals to blend into their backgrounds.

Carnivore: *(noun)* An animal that eats only meat.

Consumer: *(noun)* An organism that feeds on other organisms or particles of organic matter.

Energy (biology): *(noun)* In form of nutrients and sunlight is what sustains plants and animals in living.

Food web: *(noun)* The complex network of related food chains within an ecosystem.

Gizzard *(noun)* a muscular part of the stomachs of certain animals in which food is broken down into small pieces. Crocodiles, alligators, dinosaurs, birds, earthworms, some fish, and some crustaceans have gizzards.

Herbivore: *(noun)* An animal that only eats plants.

Niche: *(noun)* the specific role that a plant or animal has within an ecosystem; i.e., where an organism lives and how it obtains food.

Nocturnal: *(adj.)* Active during night.

Prey: *(noun)* An animal that is hunted and killed by another for food.

Primary: *(adj.)* First in order, importance, or value.

Producer: *(noun)* An organism that produces its own food and serves as a source of food for other organisms. Producers include green plants, which produce food through photosynthesis, and certain bacteria that are capable of converting inorganic substances into food through chemosynthesis.

Raptors: *(noun)* Birds of prey.

Secondary: *(adj.)* Second in order, importance, or value.

Tertiary: *(adj.)* Third in order, importance, or value.

Activity Sheet 1: Whooo's Coming for Dinner?

Name _____

Directions: Read the text, paying attention to vocabulary in bold print.

Whooo's Coming for Dinner?

Owls are **raptors**, or birds of prey. They are carnivores that have their own niche in a food chain or food web. As **tertiary consumers** at the top of a food chain, they feed exclusively on secondary consumers and have very few predators.

Owl **prey** mainly includes small mammals such as mice, rabbits, moles, or voles, but owls also eat small lizards, frogs, insects, and even other birds. In one study that scientists did over a year's time, a single Barn Owl ate approximately: 1,407 mice; 143 rats; 7 bats; 5 young rabbits; 375 house sparrows; 23 starlings; 54 other birds; 2 lizards; 174 frogs; 25 moths; and 52 crickets.

Specific **adaptations** enable an owl to hunt. While most raptors are diurnal, or active during the day, owls are **nocturnal**. Hunting at night reduces competition for prey. Like most birds of prey, owls have powerful **talons** on their feet, which enable them to easily catch and hold small animals. A sharp, thin **beak** allows an owl to tear larger prey into smaller pieces, making it easier to swallow.

Other adaptations are more unique to owls. The **camouflage** coloring and patterns of any owl's feathers allow it to blend in with its surroundings. Owls that live in forest areas have patterns that mimic the patterns in tree bark, while Snowy Owls that live in tundra areas are have white feathers.

Owls' faces are circular and relatively flat. The **feathers** around an owl's face actually gather sounds and direct them to the owl's ears. An owl can hear a mouse from nearly 75 feet away! An owl's **flight feathers** are shaped in such a way that the owl is able to fly silently. This gives the owl an advantage when pursuing prey.

One of most unique adaptations of an owl is its **eyes**. Owls can see clearly even in low light. The downward curve of an owl's beak does not block its vision when catching prey. An owl cannot move its eyes to look to the sides, but to make up for that, an owl can turn its head ¾ of the way around in either direction to see what is behind it.

Birds of prey such as owls, hawks, eagles, falcons, and harriers have no teeth to chew their food. The bird swallows its prey whole or, in the case of larger prey, in large chunks. The soft parts are then dissolved in the stomach and passed on to the intestines where the nutrients are absorbed. After that, part of the bird's stomach, called a **gizzard**, compresses the hard, non-digestible parts such as bones, teeth, fur, feathers, and insect fragments into a **pellet**, which is an elongated, egg-shaped mass. Finally, the pellet is **regurgitated**, or spit up.

Owl pellets provide valuable information about owls' seasonal, regional, and habitat preferences and conditions. Pellets also give clues about the type and number of animals, as well as the energy flow, within local **food chains** and **food webs**. Owls are found on every continent except for Antarctica. Imagine the wealth of information that could be found in a collection of "international" owl pellets!

Questions:

1. How does each owl **adaptation** help it hunt?

Talons: _____

Eyes: _____

Face Feathers: _____

Flight Feathers: _____

Beak: _____

2. Explain the term **tertiary consumer**:

_____

_____

3. What other **birds of prey** produce and regurgitate pellets?

_____

4. The first paragraph gives information about different types of animals eaten by one owl in a year's time. What can you say about the variety of food the owl ate? How might it contribute to the owl's survival?

_____

_____

_____

_____

5. Describe the process by which an **owl pellet** is formed.

First, _____

Next, _____

_____

After that, _____

_____

Finally, _____

6. What information can be gathered through the study of owl pellets?

_____

_____

_____

_____

Owl Pellet Dissection Journal

Name of Ornithologist: _____

An ornithologist is someone who studies birds!

Problem Question: What makes up an owl pellet?

Materials:

- ✓ Owl pellets
- ✓ Paper plate
- ✓ Forceps and probe
- ✓ Magnifier
- ✓ Bone Sorting Chart
- ✓ Disposable gloves
- ✓ Hand sanitizer or access to sink and soap

Predictions:

What do you think the owl pellet will look like on the outside?

_____

_____

What will you find on the inside? _____

How many different types of organisms do you think you will find? _____

Helpful Hints for Working with Owl Pellets:

1. The owl pellet has been sanitized, but be careful to wash your hands after working with it, even if you wear gloves.

2. The fur may cause people with allergies to sneeze or have a runny nose. Keep a reasonable distance between your face and the owl pellet.

3. If your pellet does not come apart easily, you can try soaking it in warm water for a few seconds.

4. Handle the bones carefully. Separate as much fur and other material away from the bone as possible.

5. The contents of each owl pellet will be different. Some pellets may have more than one skeleton, while some may have only part of a skeleton.

Procedure:

1. Measure the length, width, and mass of your owl pellet. Record your data in the *Observations* section.

2. Place the owl pellet on the paper plate. Carefully unwrap the foil and take out the pellet.

3. Use the magnifier to examine the outside of the owl pellet. Record your observations below.

4. Separate the fur from the bones using the forceps and probe.

5. Sort out the bones. Use the Bone Sorting Chart to identify them.

6. Count and record the number of each type of bone.

Observations:

1. What is the length of your owl pellet? _____ Width? _____

2. What is the weight? _____

3. How does your pellet's size compare with the rest of the pellets?

   _____

4. Use the magnifier to examine the outside of the pellet. Do you see any evidence to suggest where it may have been found? (seeds, soil, hay, twigs, small pebbles)

   _____

   _____

5. What is its color? _____

6. How can you describe the texture? _____

7. Does it have a smell? _____

8. Make a quick sketch of your owl pellet in the space below:

9. Sort out and record the number and type of bones using the Bone Sorting Chart on the next page.

Bone type	How many?	What kind of animal?
skull		
jaw		
leg		
other		

10. What types of skeletons did you find?

_____

_____

Bone Sorting Chart

	Rodent	Shrew	Mole	Bird
Skull				
Jaw				
Scapula				
Forelimb				
Hindlimb				
Pelvic bone				
Rib				
Vertebrae				

Source: **Carolina Biological Supply Company**

Activity Sheet 2: Build-a-Skeleton

Name _____

Directions: Following the procedure below, construct as many complete or partial skeletons as you can using the bones from your owl pellet.

1. Using your data and observations as well as the Bone Sorting Chart from the previous activity, review what type of bones you have, which type of prey they belong to, and how many there are.

2. Lay out the bones on a piece of construction paper and arrange them in their proper places.

3. Use liquid glue to attach each bone to the paper. They will need to be laid flat to dry overnight.

4. Label each type of bone. See the example below.

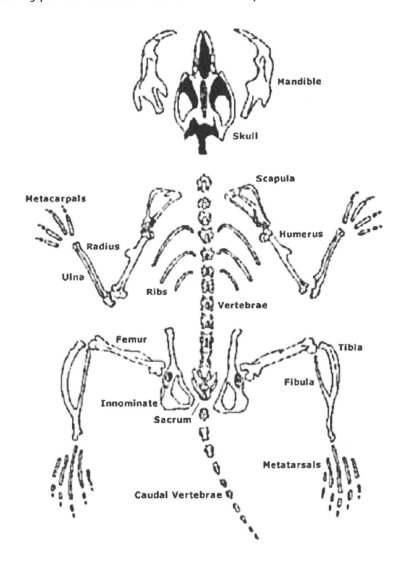

Activity Sheet 3: Owl Pellet Food Web

Name _____

Directions: Create a model of a food chain or food web using the "skeletal data" from your owl pellet. You may also work with another group who had an owl pellet with similar data to create a more extensive food web.

1. Be sure to include the following:

    ✓ Sun (source of all energy and the beginning of every food chain or web)

    ✓ Producers

    ✓ Primary Consumers

    ✓ Secondary Consumers

    ✓ Tertiary Consumers

    ✓ Decomposers (optional)

2. Here is some more information about "who eats what" in a typical owl food web:

    ✓ Mice: berries, nuts, insects, slugs

    ✓ Mole: slugs, worms

    ✓ Shrew: worms, insects

    ✓ Bird: worms, caterpillars, insects

    ✓ Vole: plants

    ✓ Worms: dead leaves or other dead material

    ✓ Insects/caterpillars: plants

    ✓ Slugs: plants, dead material, worms, other slugs

3. Here are some ideas for how your food chain or food web might look. Be creative!

Written Summary

Analysis of Food Web
FOR OWL PELLET DISSECTION

Producers: producers are mainly plants such as flowers, grass, seeds, and roots. These organisms are the basis of the food web, and is the essential key to all life because they absorb the sun's energy. They make glucose, which is eaten by other organisms.

Primary level/consumers: consumers are herbivores such as gerbils, earthworms and a variety of insects. They feed on the plants. They are the main source of meat for the predators because they contain energy made by producers.

Secondary level/Consumers: These consumers consists of carnivores and omnivores such as rodents, salamanders, and birds. They feed on the herbivores and occasionally some producers!

Tertiary level/consumers: These consumers are strictly carnivores and is represented as the owl in this food web. Their diet consists of animals from the primary and secondary levels.

Drawing

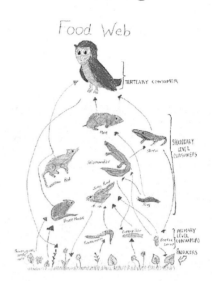

Layered Diagram

1.3 Wiggly Worms

VOCABULARY

Using correct vocabulary can help you understand science concepts better. Below are some important terms that you will learn about in *Lesson 1.3 Wiggly Worms*. Study the words and their definitions, and try to use them whenever you talk about these topics during the lesson!

Adaptation:	*(noun)* A change by which an organism or species becomes better suited to its environment.
Bacteria:	*(noun)* Microscopic living organisms.
Biodegradable:	*(adj.)* Capable of being decomposed by bacteria or other living organisms.
Castings:	*(noun)* Worm waste.
Clitellum:	*(noun)* A smooth band on the outside of the worm's body near the head end from which the cocoon is created.
Compost:	*(noun)* A mixture of decayed organic material.
Consumer:	*(noun)* An organism that feeds on other organisms or particles of organic matter.
Decomposer:	*(noun)* An organism, often a bacterium or fungus, that feeds on and breaks down dead plant or animal matter. Decomposers make essential nutrients available to plants and other organisms in the ecosystem.
Gizzard	*(noun)* a muscular part of the stomachs of certain animals in which food is broken down into small pieces. Crocodiles, alligators, dinosaurs, birds, earthworms, some fish, and some crustaceans have gizzards.
Invertebrate:	*(adj.)* An animal lacking a backbone.

Humus: *(noun)* The organic component of soil, formed by the decomposition of leaves and other plant material by soil microorganisms.

Nutrients: *(noun)* Substances such as proteins, minerals, or vitamins that are needed by people, animals, and plants to stay strong and healthy.

Reproduce: *(verb)* To make offspring.

Activity Sheet 1: Wonderings about Worms

Name _____

Directions: List everything you already know (or think you know) about worms. Then list at least three questions or "wonderings" you have about worms.

What I already know about worms	What I wonder about worms

Activity Sheet 2: Dirty Decomposers Reading

Name _____

Directions: Read the text, paying attention to the vocabulary in **bold** print. Then answer the questions on the next page.

Dirty Decomposers

Earthworms, red wigglers, night crawlers – no matter what you call them, all worms play a vital role in any food chain or food web. As **decomposers**, worms return **nutrients** from dead organisms to the soil. Worm waste, called **castings**, is rich in nutrients. Plants use these nutrients in the process of photosynthesis to make food for themselves. In turn, this provides food for **primary consumers**.

Worms also help loosen, mix, and **aerate** the soil around plant roots, as deep as 12-18 inches. Their tunnels help water move through the soil. In addition to eating organic waste, worms actually eat soil, too. The soil is broken apart and ground up in the worm's **gizzard**. The gizzard is full of fine gravel or sand that helps grind up the soil. The finely ground soil then passes through the worm's intestines. This is similar to the way a chicken's gizzard works.

The anatomy of an earthworm is adapted specifically to life underground. Worms are **invertebrates**, which means they have no backbone. Instead, their bodies are made up of hundreds of tiny rings, called **segments**. Each segment contains a muscle that enables the worm to lengthen. Another set of muscles runs lengthwise through the worm's body. The contraction and relaxation of these muscles enables the worm to move forward.

Worms' bodies are covered with **setae,** which are small, bristly hairs similar to those found on a caterpillar. The setae enable the worm to keep its place in the soil while its **musculature** (muscle system) pulls it along through the soil. A worm's body is also covered with **slime**, which allows it to slide through the earth.

Worms have **five hearts** but no lungs. They absorb oxygen through their **skin**, which is why their bodies must stay moist but not too wet. Worms have no ears, either, but can sense **vibrations** in the ground. This sense helps them know when a predator may be near. Even though they have no eyes, worms are still sensitive to light and prefer to be in dark places. They have **light-sensitive cells** in their head area which help them detect when it is night or day.

Although both ends of a worm appear to be the same, there actually is a head end and tail end. The head end is slightly pointed, while the tail end is rounder.

Probably the most unique feature of a worm's anatomy is its **reproductive parts** – it has both male and female parts. Worms cannot fertilize themselves, but they can produce eggs. Other worms must fertilize each other's eggs to produce young. A cocoon is created around the eggs in the worm's **clitellum**, which is a smooth band on the outside of the worm's body near the head end. When fertilized, the cocoon is left in the soil. Worm embryos can remain dormant in the cocoon until conditions are warm and moist enough for survival.

Worms may not be the most attractive animals, but they serve a very important role in the interdependency of the world's food webs!

Questions:

1. In what ways do worms help plants?

_____

_____

_____

_____

2. How does the fact that worms help plants fit into the food web "big picture"?

_____

_____

_____

_____

3. How are worms similar to chickens?

_____

_____

4. How do a worm's physical structures allow it to move through soil?

_____

_____

_____

_____

5. How are a worm's sense organs different from a human's sense organs?

_____

_____

_____

_____

6. What is unique about worm reproduction?

_____

_____

_____

_____

_____

7. What other questions do you have about worms?

_____

_____

_____

_____

Wiggly Worms Lab Journal

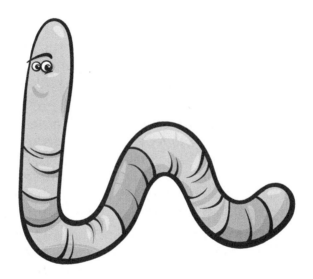

Name of Zoologist: _____

A zoologist is someone who studies animals!

Setting Up a Worm Bin

Follow these easy steps to set up a worm bin. Soon your worms will be recycling food scraps into nutrient-rich compost!

1. **Find a bin:** A deep, heavy plastic dishpan, with an approximate capacity of 14 quarts, works well for small group work. Smaller containers are easier to move around as needed. Note: If you are planning on keeping the worm bin for an extended period of time (more than three months), small ¼-inch holes should be drilled near the bottom of the dishpan. This will allow liquid, called "tea," to drain from the bin. The bin should be placed on a tray to catch the liquid. Discard the liquid if it smells bad, but if it is relatively odorless, it can be added to a garden.

2. **Prepare the bedding:** Red worms can live in moist newspaper bedding. Tear newspaper into strips about 1 inch wide. Place the strips into another large container and wet them. They should be damp, but not dripping. If they are too wet, the worms will drown. Add a few more strips of dry paper if needed. Keep some strips dry for the very top layer and in case they are needed in the future.

3. **Prepare the bin:** Add the strips to the bin until it is about ½ full, making sure the bedding is fluffy, not packed down. This provides air pockets for the worms.

4. **Add some soil:** Sprinkle 1-2 cups of outdoor or potting soil into the bin. The soil provides helpful microorganisms to the bin and it also helps worms digest their food.

5. **Add the worms:** For 8 dishpans, two pound of worms is plenty to get started with. Smaller bins need fewer worms. Gently place the worms on top of the bedding. (You will add the rest of the bedding after the food is added.)

6. **Add the food:** Put a small handful of food near the worms. Suitable food scraps for your worm bin include: ***eggshells; fruit and vegetable scraps or peels (no citrus); wilted lettuce or spinach; tea leaves; coffee grounds; leaves from outdoors; uncooked oatmeal***. Avoid onions, garlic, meat, cheese, anything salty, or watery foods such as tomatoes. Worms love ***watermelon*** and ***pumpkin***. Make sure the scraps are small in size, and bury them under the bedding. Each time the worms are fed, the scraps should be buried in a different area of the bin.

7. **Add the rest of the bedding and cover the bin:** The very top layer should be dry paper. Window screening, cheesecloth, or nylon stockings work well to cover the bin. Air should be allowed to flow freely, while keeping the worms inside.

8. **Do not add food for 1-2 weeks:** This gives the worms a chance to adjust to their new habitat, and for the food to begin to decompose. After that, you should feed the worms every three to seven days, always burying the food under the paper in a different place each time.

9. **Keep the bedding moist and aerated:** If it gets too dry, use a plant-misting bottle to add moisture. If it gets too wet, add more newspaper.

10. **Look for castings:** After three to six weeks, castings will begin to appear. The castings are actually worm waste, or "poop," which is rich in nutrients.

11. **When you are finished studying worms:** The contents of the bins may be added to a larger compost bin or garden. The compost from the worm castings will return rich nutrients to the soil.

p. 1

Worm Bin Diagram

Draw and label a diagram of your worm bin in the space below.

Safety Suggestions for All

Brainstorm, discuss, and list at least three ideas for rules the class should follow to ensure the safety of both worms and humans. Add two more rules after hearing the other groups' ideas.

1. _____

_____

2. _____

_____

3. _____

_____

4. _____

_____

5. _____

_____

p. 2

Worm Anatomy

Question: What can you observe about your worm's physical structures?

Materials:
- ✓ Worms
- ✓ Viewing container
- ✓ Absorbent paper towel
- ✓ Water
- ✓ Magnifier
- ✓ Ruler

Procedure:
1. Moisten the paper towel and fit it into the bottom of the viewing container.
2. Gently place a worm into the container. Make sure the paper towel (and the worm!) stays moist.
3. Record your observations.

Observations:
1. What color is your worm? _____

2. Gently touch the worm. How does its skin feel?

   _____

3. Gently turn your worm over. What differences do you observe between the topside and underside?

   _____

   _____

4. How long is your worm? _____

5. Worms are made up of segments. Compare your worm to another worm that has a different length. Which worm appears to have more segments, the longer worm or the shorter worm?

   _____

p. 3

6. Using a magnifier, locate each exterior part of the worm in the diagram.

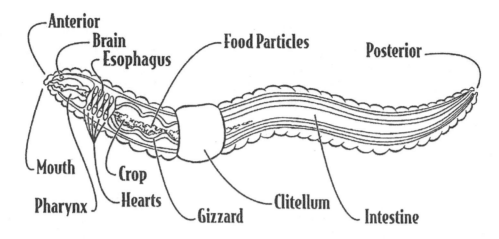

7. Can you determine the anterior (head) and posterior (tail) ends of the worm? **Yes / No**

8. Can you locate the clitellum on your worm? (If your worm is too young, the clitellum may not be developed enough.) **Yes / No**

9. Use the outline of the worm below to show your worm's coloring.

10. What other observations did you make?

_____

_____

_____

_____

Worm Movements

Question: How does your worm move? A worm's shape and mucus (slime) help it slide and move. The segments of a worm, along with its longitudinal muscles, contract and relax to allow the worm to lengthen and shorten. The setae, or bristle-like structures, are arranged around each segment. They help the worm grip the surrounding area as it moves, providing traction.

Materials:
- ✓ Worms
- ✓ Sheet of copy paper
- ✓ Smooth, clean surface, such as a tabletop
- ✓ Viewing container
- ✓ Absorbent paper towel
- ✓ Water
- ✓ Magnifier

Procedure:
1. Carefully place the worm onto the copy paper.

2. Use the magnifier to look for the setae around each segment.

3. Wait for the worm to start to move across the paper. Lean down close to the paper and listen for a faint scraping noise as the setae brush across the paper.

4. Moisten the paper towel and fit it into the bottom of the viewing container. Place the worm into the container to allow it to moisten.

5. Carefully remove the worm and place it on the smooth table surface and watch it move.

6. Record your observations.

Observations:
1. What did you observe as the worm moved across the copy paper? Did you hear the scraping of the setae?

_____

_____

2. What did you observe as the worm moved across the tabletop?

_____

_____

p. 5

Worm Reactions

Question #1: How do worms react to wet vs. dry surfaces?

Materials:
- ✓ Worms
- ✓ Viewing container
- ✓ Absorbent paper towels
- ✓ Water

Procedure:
1. Wet one piece of paper towel, and spread it on one half of the viewing container.

2. Spread the dry towel on the other half of the container. Make sure the edges overlap slightly, with the moist paper towel on top.

3. Place one worm (or more) on the dry side, near the overlap.

4. Record your observations.

Observations:

Dry side	Wet side

What did the worm do when placed on the dry surface? _____

_____

Do worms seems to prefer the moist or dry surface?_____

What other observations did you make?_____

_____

_____

p. 6

Question #2: How do worms react to light?

Note: This activity may require "wait time" to allow the worms to move.

Materials:
- ✓ Cardboard box with lid
- ✓ Worms
- ✓ Paper towel, moistened

Procedure:
1. Cut the lid of the box in half so that it covers half of the box.
2. Line the bottom of the entire box with a moistened paper towel.
3. Place the worms in the uncovered side of the box.
4. Observe the worms.

Observations:
Use the box outline below to show the movement of the worms:

1. How do the worms react to being placed on the uncovered side?

_____

2. What other observations did you make? _____

_____

p. 7

Question #3: How do worms react to touch or vibrations?

Materials:
- ✓ Worms
- ✓ Viewing container or clean tabletop
- ✓ Pencil

Procedure:
1. Read, carry out, and respond to each question below.

2. Record your observations.

Observations:
1. Hold a worm gently in your hand. What does it do? _____

_____

2. Gently touch the head end and then the tail end. What does the worm do?

   Head end touch: _____

   Tail end touch: _____

3. What happens when you tap a pencil on the edge of the container, or on the table near the worm?

_____

_____

4. Place another worm in contact with your worm. How does your worm respond?

_____

_____

5. Place the pencil as an obstacle in front of your worm as it moves. How does the worm respond?

_____

_____

p. 8

Question #4: Do worms have a sense of smell?

Materials:
- ✓ Worms
- ✓ Cotton balls
- ✓ Flat surface (tabletop or viewing container)
- ✓ Paper towels, moistened
- ✓ "Test substances" such as: vinegar, nail polish remover, water, pure extracts

It smells funny in here

Procedure:
Remember, humane treatment of worms is absolutely necessary at all times! Substances should **never** touch the worms themselves.

1. Place the worm(s) on the flat, moistened surface.

2. Dip a cotton ball into the first test substance, and hold it about 1 cm from the worm's head.

3. Record the worm's reaction to the substance in the chart below.

4. Use the same procedure at the worm's tail end. Record the worm's reaction.

5. Continue with each of the test substances and record your observations.

Observations:

Test Substance	Head-end Reaction			Tail-end Reaction		
	No reaction	Moved toward	Moved Away	No reaction	Moved toward	Moved Away
Ex: vinegar			X	X		

How can your further describe the worm's reactions? What did their body do?

_____

_____

p. 9

Compost Bin Observations

Date: _____

_____

_____

_____

Date: _____

_____

_____

_____

Date: _____

_____

_____

_____

Date: _____

_____

_____

_____

Date: _____

_____

_____

_____

Extra Notes on Worms & Composting

_____

_____

_____

_____

_____

_____

_____

_____

_____

_____

_____

_____

_____

_____

Activity Sheet 3: Composting

Name _____

Directions: Read the text, paying attention to any vocabulary in **bold** print. On the following page, list important details under the main idea heading of each paragraph.

What is Composting?

Do you know what happens to your garbage? Hopefully you do not throw it all into the trashcan. Some can be recycled, some can reused, and some can be composted. All organic material is **biodegradable**. That means it decomposes, or decays. A **compost pile** is nature's way of recycling and reusing organic (living) waste materials from plants. Composting speeds up the decay process. Adding compost to a garden helps grow stronger, healthier plants.

Getting Started

Starting your own compost pile is easy! Choose a corner of your garden for your pile. Make sure it will receive direct sunlight for a good part of the day. You can buy a compost bin or use a large wooden box that does not have a top. Now just fill the bin with grass clippings, leaves, shredded newspaper, vegetable and fruit peelings, eggshells, coffee grounds, and even tea leaves. Do not add any weeds unless you want weeds growing in your garden. Do not put any animal products in the compost pile. Products like meat, cheese, or other dairy products take too long to decompose and may attract unwanted animal visitors.

Nature will add worms and other creatures such as beetles, fungi, and bacteria to the pile to help it along. As decomposers eat the food material, it is processed through their bodies. The decomposers' waste material will return nutrients to the soil.

Maintaining the Compost Pile

Taking care of the compost pile is easy, too, since nature does most of the work. Sun and rain provide necessary heat and water. As the pile starts to compost it will heat up to an internal temperature of 130 to 140 degrees Fahrenheit. This means everything is working as it should. You can measure the temperature using a thermometer or even your hand. If the middle of the pile feels very warm to the touch, it is ready to "turn."

Use a pitchfork or a shovel to mix up the pile once or twice a week. Air is another necessary ingredient for composting. **Turning the pile** allows air to get into it. Aerating also keeps the top from getting too wet and smelly. After a few weeks, **humus** will be visible. Humus is the final product of composting.

It is dark, crumbly, and cool to the touch. It is also full of nutrients and helps soil retain water. You can collect the humus and add it to garden soil.

Why Compost?

A compost pile has many benefits. It keeps waste that can be useful out of landfills (and may lower disposal costs). A compost pile provides natural fertilizer for your yard, garden, or houseplants. Exploring the compost pile can also be educational, as you watch decomposers help transform waste material into soil.

Building a compost pile is a win-win for everyone!

Directions: List the main idea and 3-4 details under the heading for each paragraph.

Paragraph 1: Introduction

Main Idea: _____

Details:

- _____
- _____
- _____
- _____

Paragraph 2: Getting Started

Main Idea: _____

Details:

- _____
- _____
- _____
- _____

Paragraph 3: Maintaining the Compost Pile

Main Idea: _____

Details:

- _____
- _____
- _____
- _____

Paragraph 4: Why Compost?

Main Idea: _____

Details:

- _____
- _____
- _____
- _____

Activity Sheet 4: Spread the Word!

Name _____

Spread the Word about Composting!

You are now experts in worm anatomy and behavior, and know all about how worms assist in composting. Create a persuasive project to convince your audience about the benefits of "vermicomposting" (using worms, microorganisms, and other living things to decompose materials). Read the descriptions of each project, and then pick one to complete and share. Be creative!

1. **Composting Presentation**: Teach a group about the benefits of composting.

   a. Make a list of 6 key points (no more) that you want to address about composting. Divide the information into sub groups, such as:

      ✓ *What is composting?*
      ✓ *How does it work?*
      ✓ *What are the benefits?*

   Leave time at the end for the audience to ask questions. You might want to generate a list of possible questions so that you're ready to answer them.

   b. Decide on the role of each group member. Someone (or two people) needs to talk, and someone else can design visuals.

   c. Rehearse in your small group, and then practice in front of willing volunteers who will give helpful feedback. Pay attention to timing (don't talk for too long!) and make sure each person who wants to talk has about the same amount of time.

   d. Invite your audience! This might include parents, other classes, administrators, or even community members or the local gardening club. The public library may be willing to help with space and a time.

   e. After your presentation, be sure to discuss what went well and what you might work on improving for a future presentation. Good Luck!

2. Composting Pamphlet: Create a pamphlet that explains the benefits of composting.

   a. Make a list of 6 key points (no more) that you want to address about composting. Divide the information into sub groups, such as:

   - ✓ *What is composting?*
   - ✓ *How does it work?*
   - ✓ *What are the benefits?*
   - ✓ *Frequently Asked Questions...* Think of possible questions that someone might have about this topic, and provide answers in the pamphlet.

   b. Find and read examples of informational pamphlets. What kind of information is presented, and how is it presented? How is it laid out on the page? Do special text features, illustrations, or other graphics help the reader understand the information better?

   c. Make a sketch of your pamphlet layout. Where will each key point be located on the page? How much space can be allowed for each section? How long can the text be? Will you include special text features, illustrations, or other graphics?

   d. Assign one section to each group member to draft (you can also work in pairs).

   e. When everyone is ready, share your ideas. Give positive suggestions and then revise.

   f. Check in one more time for final feedback and edits.

   g. Decide how the pamphlet will be produced. Will you use a computer, write/draw by hand, or use another method?

   h. Make copies of the pamphlets. Who will be your audience? Where will the pamphlets be placed?

   i. Find a place to distribute the pamphlets. The public library may be willing to set up an area where community members can pick up copies of your pamphlet.

3. **Video Public Service Announcement:** Create a brief video presentation (two to three minutes long) to promote composting in your community.

   a. Make a list of 6 key points (no more) that you want to address about composting. Divide the information into sub groups, such as:

      ✓ *What is composting?*
      ✓ *How does it work?*
      ✓ *What are the benefits?*
      ✓ *Frequently Asked Questions...* Think of possible questions that someone might have about this topic, and provide answers in the video.

   b. With the help of an adult, find and watch a few short public service announcements to get an idea about length and how material is presented.

   c. Make a plan for your video. What will you talk about? Where will the video be shown? Who is your intended audience?

   d. Decide on the role of each group member. Someone (or two people) needs to talk, and someone else can design visuals.

   e. Write a script that addresses each of your key points. You can choose to do a direct presentation (where one or two people has a part to talk about) or an interview situation (where someone asks questions and someone else answers).

   f. Choose a background for your video. Decide on relevant visuals or props that will not distract from the information.

   g. Rehearse in your small group, and then practice in front of volunteers who will give helpful feedback. Pay attention to timing (don't talk for too long!) and make sure each person who wants to talk has about the same amount of time.

   h. Time to make the video! You may need to do multiple "takes" to get it perfect. Someone may lose their place, forget whose turn it is, or maybe even get a bit silly. Watch each take until you get it the way you want it.

   i. Submit your video, and wait for feedback!

4. Marketing Products: Create a poster, bumper sticker, t-shirt, or hat design to promote composting.

a. Bring in examples of t-shirts, hats, or bumper stickers from home that promote local (or other) products. Study the main message... How many words are used to convey it? Are there any graphics, illustrations, or special text features? Can you find any existing products that promote composting?

b. Decide on one or two different products for your group to "produce."

c. Draft your message, and choose any visual information (special text features or images). Keep it simple!

d. Draw several sketches of your idea, and then as a group choose the one that works best.

e. Work on your final copy. Are there resources in your school that you can use to actually print a poster, t-shirt, bumper sticker, or hat design? Many word processing programs can be used in conjunction with iron-on materials to create a final shirt or hat product. Ask your teacher about what is available.

f. Present your project! Ask your teacher if you can display your project around the school or (if you've made a clothing item) wear it during the day.

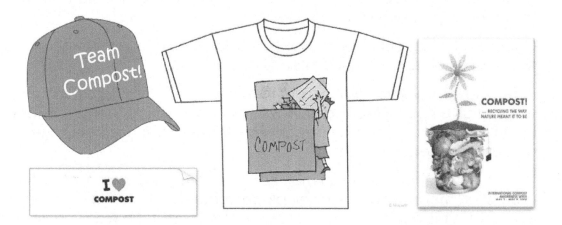